Into the Storm

by

Stephen Potts

Illustrated by Nigel Dobbyn

For Emily

WORCESTERSHIRE COUNTY COUNCIL	
282	
Bertrams	17.02.08
	£5.99
WS	

First published in 2008 in Great Britain by
Barrington Stoke Ltd
18 Walker Street, Edinburgh, EH3 7LP

www.barringtonstoke.co.uk

ISBN: 978-1-84299-516-7

Printed in Great Britain by Bell & Bain Ltd

Contents

Chapter 1
The Journey Begins

Dad put down his mobile phone. "Uncle John's car has broken down," he told me. "Looks like it's just you and me, David. What do you think?"

I looked round. We were sitting in our little sailing boat called *Puffin*, safely tied up on a mooring in a small Scottish town. The weather was good. There was enough wind to sail, but not so much as to make the water rough.

We had never sailed with just the two of us before. Dad and Uncle John always knew what to do, whatever the wind and weather were doing. I would watch them, and join in when it was calm, but I'd always been just a spare pair of hands. Now Dad was asking if I was ready to be a crew-man. A real sailor.

"I think we'll be fine," I told him.

He smiled. "I hoped you would say that. But remember, you have to do what I say – nothing more, nothing less. OK?"

"OK!"

"Right, then. Let's get the boat ready."

We checked the boat one last time. We made sure the fuel tank was full, the batteries were charged, and the hatches were

closed. We checked the safety gear – first aid kit, fire extinguisher, signal flares – and we got the charts ready to use. Dad handed me my life-jacket. I had never found it easy to put on, but now I was a real sailor, not just a passenger, so I had to get it right first time. I slipped it over my head, clipped the buckle shut, and smiled. "Ready," I said.

"Would you like to call the coast-guard?"

"Yeah!" I said. He had never let me use the radio before, but it looked easy enough.

"Good. You call them up, then hand over to me."

I put the mike to my lips and pressed the transmit button. "Clyde Coast-guard, this is *Puffin*, over."

The radio loud-speaker crackled into life. The coast-guard was talking to me! *"Puffin,* this is Clyde Coast-guard. Stand by on channel 10, over."

I handed the mike to Dad and he gave the rest of the message, telling the coast-guard we were going to Oban, 30 miles away.

When he finished, he switched the engine on. It started first time. I went up front to the bow of the boat and started to undo the rope that tied us onto our mooring. The rope was thick and heavy, with smelly, slimy sea-weed still stuck all over, but I didn't mind grabbing it. That's just what sailors have to do.

"Let go forward!" called Dad. I slid the rope off and dropped it into the water. Dad let the wind push us backwards, until we were free of the mooring, then set the engine to forward, and pointed our bow towards the open sea. We were off!

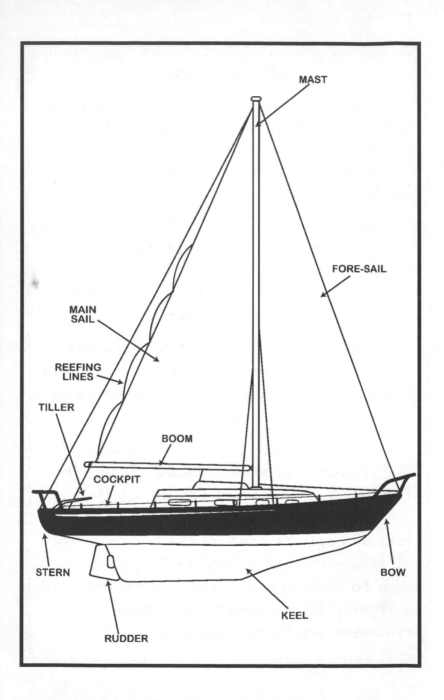

PARTS OF A BOAT

The pointed front is the <u>bow</u>. The round back is the <u>stern</u>. The right side of the boat is called <u>starboard</u>, and has a green light. The left side is called <u>port</u>, and has a red light.

The tall pole that holds the sail up is the <u>mast</u>. At the bottom of the mast is another pole called the <u>boom</u>. Most small boats have two sails - the <u>fore-sail</u> at the front, and the <u>main-sail</u> behind.

The hull is the main part of the boat. At the bottom, under the water, is a heavy fin called the <u>keel</u>. It keeps the boat upright when the wind pushes against the sails.

The place where you sit is the <u>cockpit</u>. This is where you steer the boat from. The Puffin has a pole called a <u>tiller</u>, which is joined to the <u>rudder</u> for steering. There are lots of ropes to control the sails, and they all have different names. <u>Reefing lines</u> are used to make the sail smaller, when the wind is strong. It can sometimes be hard to remember what rope does what job!

Chapter 2
The Corry

Our sails were up, our engine was off, and we were speeding along on a lovely day. The sky was high and clear and blue. The sun shone warmly on my face, and sun-light sparkled off the low rolling waves, marked here and there by white caps of foam. Apart from some other boats, a few miles behind, we were alone on the water.

To our left (to port, remember!), were scattered the islands, as far as I could see.

Some were just rocks sticking up out of the water. Others were low and long, flat and green, dotted with white sheep and red Highland cows. Others still were huge mountains, rising up out of the sea all the way to the clouds.

Dad pointed to one of them. Cloud sat on its top like a big white hat, and a tiny house clung to the hill-side below the cloud. "Do you remember that island's name?" he asked me.

I scratched my head. We had sailed past many times before, but the islands' names were strange, and not easy to remember. I knew that the island called Luing was nearby, and so was Seil. I had a feeling the name began with S.

"Seil," I guessed.

He smiled but shook his head. "No. That's Seil." He pointed to another island, and then back at the first one. "This one is called Scarba."

I remembered now. "Of course," I said.

"Have another look at the charts, and tell me what we have to be really careful about round here."

CHARTS

Maps of the sea are called <u>charts</u>. A real sailor would never call them maps. They show the land with landmarks you can see from the water, like big chimneys and radio masts. They also show how deep the sea is by using different colours.

I went down into the cabin and looked at the big paper map – sorry, chart – laid out on the table. The land was yellow, and the edges of the sea were dark or light blue. Most of the sea was just white, but covered in

numbers which tell you how deep it is. There was lots of other information on the chart, along with the names of all the islands.

I looked at Scarba. The nearest island to it was called Jura. Between them was a channel marked "Danger!" It had a long name I could not read. I just looked at the first part of the name, and when I thought I knew how to say it I went back up to the cockpit.

"We have to be careful of the Corry – the Corry-something," I told Dad.

"That's right. The Corryvreckan. We'll just call it the Corry. The tide runs very fast there and it can be very rough when the wind is strong. When it's bad there's a huge whirl-pool, one of the biggest in the world. It could suck down a boat as small as ours. We're going to keep at least five miles away."

TIDES

If you've been to the seaside you will know that the sea goes up and down. Sometimes it can be really <u>high</u>, so it covers the beaches and the rocks. If you wait a while - six hours - it will then be <u>low</u>, so you can walk a long way out over the beach before you get to the water. And six hours later it will be high again. These are the different tides, called - wait for it! - <u>high tide</u> and <u>low tide</u>.

The sea doesn't just go up and down. When the tide falls the water has to go somewhere, so it moves side-ways. In most places it doesn't move fast. But in some narrow channels, or gaps between islands, the water has to squeeze through, like when you put your thumb on the end of a hose to make a spray. In these places the tide can run very fast, and the water can get very rough. The worst place in Britain for this is the Corry!

Chapter 3
Dolphins

Dad let me steer the boat for a while.
I felt like a real sailor, sitting at the back (in the stern, as sailors say), with my hands on the thick wooden tiller. To steer straight, I had to pull the tiller towards me as we went up the waves, then push it away as we went down again. When there is nothing but sea nearby, it's not easy to be sure you are going in a straight line – there's nothing to point at! So I kept my eyes on the compass, which

HOW TO NAVIGATE - WHERE ARE WE?

To navigate, you need ways of knowing where you are, how fast you're going, and where you want to get to. Every place in the world has a <u>latitude</u> and <u>longitude</u>. These words are too tricky for me, so I call them <u>lat</u> and <u>long</u>. If you can measure these, you know just where you are, and you can point to the place on a chart.

If there is a landmark (like a lighthouse, a rock, an island) nearby, you can point a compass at it, and measure the direction it's in. This is called <u>taking a bearing</u>. If you get three bearings on different landmarks, and draw lines on the chart, the place where the lines cross tells you where you are. This is called <u>taking a fix</u>. If you are not near land, there won't be any landmarks, but you can use an object called a <u>sextant</u> to work out the position of the sun in the day, or the moon and stars at night, to do the same.

told me that we were on the course that Dad had told me to keep.

The *Puffin* had a little electronic screen near the compass. This was our GPS (Global Positioning System). It had a picture of the sea and islands, just like the paper chart in the cabin. It also had a little arrow showing where we were, and there were lots of numbers to tell us which way we were going, how fast, how far we had to go, and when we would get there. Without it we would have to take our own bearings and do lots of tricky sums to find all this out.

Real sailors still have to know how to use these old ways to navigate, in case their GPS fails. Dad was good at it, but it wasn't easy for me, however hard I tried, so I was glad we had the GPS. I thought about sailors in the old days who often didn't even have charts, never mind gadgets like ours – but they still went round the world in their creaky wooden ships.

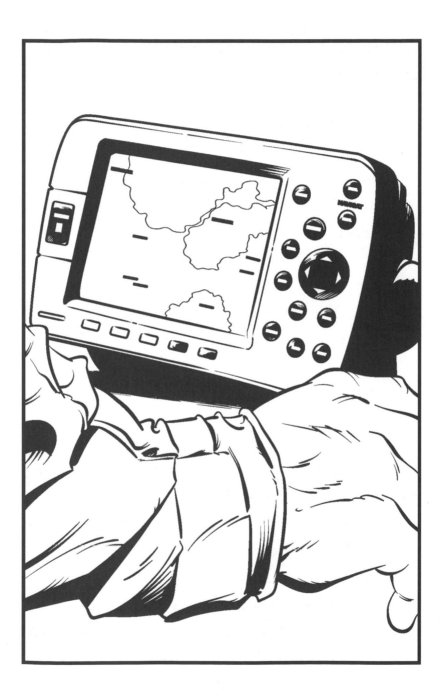

HOW TO NAVIGATE - WHERE ARE WE GOING?

Modern boats have tiny propellers joined to the hull under water. They spin round as the boat moves through the water, and you can measure your speed by checking how fast they spin.

To work out how to get to where you want, you have to know how far away it is, how fast you are going, which way the tide is pushing you, and whether the wind is sending you off course. When you've done all the sums, you will have a <u>course to steer</u> - the direction you have to point the boat in.

But the sums are not easy, and you sometimes need to look things up in large books full of numbers. This is not an easy thing to do if you are cold, and hungry and tired. The GPS does this for you - and it doesn't get seasick!

Something in the water caught my eye, and I looked away from the compass for a moment. There was a dark grey fin cutting fast through the water towards our boat!

"Dad!" I called. The first fin vanished, but two more came up, one on each side of it.

"Dolphins!" said Dad. "A whole family of them."

They passed behind the boat, so close that we could hear them breathe in loud puffs. I could even see the blow holes on the top of their heads open and close. They went on, diving between the waves, until we could not see them any more, but we stared after them for a long time.

I sniffed. There was a strange smell, which didn't fit, out here at sea. A smell of smoke. I looked around, but saw nothing.

It was getting stronger, and now Dad could smell it too. He looked into the cabin. A curl of smoke passed up the steps, over Dad's head, and I could see the flicker of orange flames inside. I gasped, and felt my chest clamp tight with fear. We were on fire!

Chapter 4
On Fire!

Everything happened in a blur. Dad shouted at me to hold our course, while he grabbed a fire extinguisher and dashed down the steps. I gripped the tiller tight, and fixed my eyes on the compass. My heart beat like a galloping horse.

The smoke was coming up in thick clouds now, and I heard Dad cough. He shouted again, but I couldn't hear what he said. I

couldn't leave the tiller, because someone had to control the boat. "Dad?" I called to him, but I knew he wouldn't hear me.

The smoke got thicker and thicker, and below it the flames were bigger and redder than before. I quickly looked round. There was no other boat in sight, and the nearest land was miles away. We had to fight the fire on our own.

Then I heard a hiss, and I knew Dad had got the fire extinguisher going. The hiss went on and on, very loudly, but the flames were soon gone, and the cloud of smoke got thinner. Then I heard another shout, and a loud thump, and the hissing suddenly stopped. Everything was silent.

I looked away from the compass to the inside of the boat. There was only a thin wisp of smoke, and that soon died away. The fire was out, but I couldn't see Dad. I called to

him, but he didn't reply. I shouted, but nothing came back.

I thought hard to work out what to do. I had to go inside, to find out what had happened, but if I left the tiller the boat might swing round, and let the wind tip us over. I lifted the lid of a little cupboard nearby, and felt inside it with my free hand, till I found what I was looking for. A piece of thin rope. I pulled it out and wrapped the middle part of it round and round the tiller, then tied each end to the side of the boat, so the tiller would not move. I let it go, to check the boat would still steer straight, then went to the steps, scared of what I would find inside.

It was a mess. Smoke had made everything black and greasy, and fire had eaten away some of the wood near the engine. Dad lay on the floor, which was slippy with fire extinguisher foam.

I felt for his pulse, like I had been shown in first aid class. It was OK, and he was breathing all right, but there was a big bump on his head where he had hit the table when he fell. I shook his arm and shouted in his ear. "Dad!" I yelled – but he didn't say anything. He was out cold.

I thought it was best to leave him where he was, but I put a pillow under his head, and used more pillows to stop him rolling about as the boat moved. When he was safe I went back to the tiller, to check my rope was working, while I worked out what to do next.

We needed help. I didn't know how much damage the fire had done, but I did know I couldn't sail the boat alone, and Dad looked like he needed to go to hospital. I knew that the radio had an emergency button. All I had to do was press it, and a life-boat would be on its way in minutes.

CALLING FOR HELP

New boat radios have a way to send a signal to the coast-guard by pressing one button. The signal tells them straight away that you need help. It is linked to the boat's GPS, so at the same time it tells the coast-guard right where you are.

 If this doesn't work, you can still send a <u>mayday</u> call by speaking on the radio. The name comes from a French word which means "help me". As well as the coast-guard and the life-boats, any other boats nearby have to stop what they are doing to help you.

You can also get help by using <u>flares</u>. Some you shoot up into the sky and they float down under parachutes. Others are flares you hold. Some of them burn bright white, to use in the dark. Others make a lot of orange smoke, to use in the day. Some of them float, so you can chuck them onto the water to make smoke.

You can also use flashing lights to send a message in <u>Morse code</u>, where the letters of the alphabet are turned into long or short flashes. The code for the letter S is three short flashes (- - -), and the code for O is three long ones (— — —). To ask for help you flash the code for S.O.S., which stands for "Save Our Souls". You can also use short and long blasts of noise, like from a whistle or a fog-horn.

****

I went back inside, took a deep breath and pushed the button. Nothing happened. I pushed it again. Still nothing. Then I checked the radio itself. I picked up the mike and pressed the transmit switch. "Clyde Coast-guard, this is *Puffin*. Mayday, mayday, mayday. Over." Nothing.

I flicked the switches on the radio. No lights came on, and no sound came out. It wasn't working. I tried all the other switches, for the lights, the fridge, the depth sounder, everything. Nothing worked.

I started to panic. The fire must have destroyed everything electrical. And that would include the GPS. I flicked the switches and pressed the buttons, but the screen

stayed blank. The last switch I tried was the engine, but I knew by now it wasn't going to start – and it didn't.

So here I was, drifting past the Corry, sailing a boat on my own, with no GPS, no engine, no radio, no lights, and my dad still out cold inside. I was in trouble.

I scratched my head, thinking about the safety checks Dad always went through before we set off. Of course! Flares! I opened a locker in the cockpit and pulled out a yellow plastic box. I took off the lid, and pulled out some long things that looked like big fire-works. I knew there were different kinds, and I read the writing on them with care until I was sure I had the one I wanted and I knew how to use it.

I pointed the long yellow tube into the wind and up into the sky, and hit the bottom of it hard with my other hand. There was a

loud pop, followed by a whoosh, and a blinding white flash, as a rocket shot out of the tube and up into the sky. When my eyes started working again a few seconds later, there was a bright light hanging from a parachute high above my little boat. As it drifted slowly down to the sea, I said to myself over and over, "Someone has to see it. Someone has to see it."

When the flare hit the sea and fizzled out I felt even more alone. Someone might have seen it, but the nearest life-boat station was 20 miles away, so even if a life-boat set off right away it would take an hour or more to arrive. And who knew where we would be by then.

I knew I had to keep sailing the boat, and do what I could to navigate. I got the hand compass out and pointed it at the top of Scarba, which looked a lot closer now. I wrote down the bearing on my hand, then pointed

it at the light-house away to starboard, and
wrote that bearing down too.

Then I pointed the compass at a big white
building ten miles behind. I went down to the
chart table and drew lines from the three
landmarks using my bearings. The lines
crossed over at a place much closer to the
gap between Scarba and Jura than I wanted
to be.

I shook Dad's arm.

"Dad," I said. "Dad! The tide is taking us
into the Corry! You have to wake up now."

He didn't.

Chapter 5
The Whirl-pool

I went back to the cockpit, and pulled the tiller to steer the boat away, but I could soon tell it was no use. The tide was pushing us faster than we could sail. I waited 15 minutes, then I took the same bearings as before, and I drew more lines on the chart. It was clear now. We were being swept towards the Corry, no matter how hard I tried to steer away.

I felt cold and shivery, even though the sun was still out, and when I looked behind I grew colder still. Dark clouds were piling up, and I could feel the wind getting stronger. The weather was getting worse.

I pushed the tiller and pointed our bow right at the Corry. We had to get through quickly, before the wind got really strong.

I tied the tiller and went back inside. I packed pillows and sleeping bags all round Dad, and I put away everything that might fly around when it got rough. I put on extra clothes, and my heavy water-proofs.

I found a harness – a short strong rope with clips on both ends. I went back to the cockpit, and closed the hatch behind me. I didn't want any big waves going down inside. I clipped one end of the harness to my life-jacket, and the other end to the side of the boat. I didn't want to be washed off the boat if it got really rough.

The waves were growing bigger as the tide got faster and the wind blew harder. It was getting difficult to control the boat, and I knew I had to pull in the sails, to make them smaller (sailors call this reefing). I was glad I could do this from the cockpit without having to go up to the mast, but I had to remember which were the right ropes to pull to make it happen.

The fore-sail was easy – it just rolled up until it was half its normal size – but the main-sail was harder. It took a long time, and a lot of effort, and once I nearly lost control of the boat – but I did it.

I was breathing hard and really tired when I finished – and not a moment too soon, because the wind was beginning to shriek in the rigging over-head, and the waves were high all round us. The tops of the waves were foamy and white, and some of the foam blew off to fill the air. Every few seconds I would get hit by a bucket-full of cold, salty water, stinging my eyes and running down inside my water-proofs.

I looked around. "It was Force 4 when we set off," I said. "And it's Force 6 now."

I didn't feel quite so alone, or so scared, when I heard a human voice, even though I knew it was my own. I wanted to keep talking

out loud, and even singing until we got through this. I looked round again. "Nope. It's Force 7 now, and it's still getting stronger."

WIND

Many years ago a man called Sir Francis Beaufort invented a scale to tell how strong the wind is. The best wind for sailing is a Force 3 (light breeze) or Force 4 (moderate breeze). Once it gets to Force 6 (strong breeze) it is pretty tricky in a small boat like ours.

In a Force 8 (gale) you wouldn't want to be out, even in a big boat. At Force 10 (storm) a big ship might have problems, and in Force 12 (hurricane) even the biggest, most powerful ships in the world could sink.

Storms are noisy. The wind whistles in your ears, screams in the mast, and makes anything loose flap loudly. Waves roar when their tops break into white surf, and the spray slaps hard when it hits people and boats. When boats race through the water they make a kind of singing sound, and they slam into big waves with loud bangs.

I had to sing at the top of my voice to hear anything above all this racket. I ran through all the songs I knew, and shouted nonsense to fill the gaps when I couldn't remember the words.

"Always look on the bright side of life," I sang, as loud as I could, over and over. My mouth didn't work properly to whistle, so I just shouted. "Da-dum. Da-dum-da-da-da-dum."

I clung to the tiller, pushing and pulling as hard as I could, to keep the boat straight as we bounced from wave to wave, and rolled one way and then the other. Sometimes we rolled so far the water came pouring into the cockpit, and then when we came upright, it poured out again. I was cold and tired and alone, and hungry and wet and very, very scared. There was nothing else I could do but hold on, and steer, and sing.

"Always look on the bright –" A huge roar, as if from a hundred sea-monsters, filled the air all round me. In a panic, I looked to see where it came from, but saw nothing. It was from everywhere. And then there was a break in the waves and I saw it. A huge whirl-pool, away off to starboard.

The waves rose high on all sides, and the black water swirled round a foaming white centre which sank down into the deep. It was like a giant plug-hole in the sea, and my little boat was the tiny speck which was going to go down it.

I had no breath left for singing now. I pulled the tiller hard over, to try and steer the boat away, and I lay on top of it to hold it there. I tried not to think how deep that plughole went. I wondered if anyone would find the wreck of our boat. Would anyone know how hard I had fought to save her?

The roaring grew louder and the water rougher still. I was thrown around like a rag doll, getting battered and bruised, but clinging onto the tiller as if my life depended on it. Which it did.

I didn't look at the whirl-pool – I didn't want to see it – until the roaring didn't seem so close now. It wasn't off to starboard any more. I looked back to see the angry mouth of the whirl-pool opening and closing half a mile away. Half a mile behind us! We'd got past. Maybe we could get through the Corry after all.

The water was still very rough, and the wind strong, but it had stopped getting worse. I was able to sit up, and I could control the tiller without having to lie on top of it. For the first time I thought about what was on the other side of the Corry. I tried to remember what the charts showed, but it was still far too risky to leave the tiller and go inside and look at them.

I could see, between the buckets of spray, that the tip of the island Jura stretched away to the south, on our port side. If I followed it round there would be some shelter from the wind and the tide. But I knew I had better not get too close, in case there were any rocks sticking up.

I steered the boat south, getting further away from the whirl-pool. Slowly the wind dropped, the waves got smaller, and the noise fell away. As soon as it was safe I tied the tiller, opened the hatch, and went inside.

I worried what state Dad would be in, but he looked really peaceful, among the pillows, covered in sleeping bags, and breathing softly.

"Lucky so and so," I said, as I looked at the charts.

There wasn't any time for taking bearings, but I could see that we were nearing a bay where the water got shallow and ran up onto a sandy beach. There was a sign on the chart like a drawing of a boat's anchor. "There!" I yelled. "We'll be safe there!"

The wind was still strong enough to push us fast toward the beach, so I pulled in the sails, then went forward to the bow. We had a heavy anchor tied on with tight knots. My fingers were too cold to untie the knots, so I got out my knife and cut through them. I looked up to see waves breaking on the beach, not far away.

"I'm not sailing this boat through the Corry just to wreck her on that beach!" I said.

The anchor was linked to a thick chain which went through a hole in the deck. I pulled out the chain until, at a guess, there

was about 20 metres of it laid out on the deck. Then I threw the anchor over the bow and into the water.

There was a big splash, and the chain ran out very quickly. There was a sudden shock as the anchor dug into the sea-bed, and the chain pulled tight. I was thrown onto my back, getting more bruises, but when I got up we had come to a stop, 40 metres from the shore. The anchor was holding. We were safe.

Chapter 6
Rescue

I stood at the bow, after checking the anchor yet again. The sun was nearly down, and a fog was rolling in. Already I couldn't see across to Scarba, and soon I'd lose sight of the nearby beach. I had one flare left, which I was saving in case a boat came past. By now people must be searching for us – but would they think to look here, in this bay so far away? I shivered and went down to the cabin.

Dad was groaning and moving around a bit. We had no electric power, and I wanted to save the batteries in my torch, so I lit the oil lamp. Despite all my extra clothes I was getting cold. The gas cooker was still working, so I lit it and sat down to wait for the kettle to boil.

There was a low humming noise. I lifted the kettle but the noise didn't stop, and soon I was sure. The noise came from outside. I scrambled on deck, but couldn't see a thing. It was fully dark, and the fog was now really thick. I didn't think even a flare would work now – but the noise was still there and getting louder, and I knew it was a boat engine.

I grabbed a fog-horn from the locker, and pressed the button. The blast was so loud next to my ear that it hurt. I remembered the signal for SOS and held the fog-horn at arm's length. Three short blasts, then three long, then three short. I listened. The engine was still there, and maybe getting closer.

I blasted out SOS again, and this time when I stopped to listen I heard another fog-horn answer me. I didn't know enough Morse code to tell what message they sent, but they had heard me, and they were coming to help. I tried to signal again, but the fog-horn was running out of gas.

I heard the kettle whistle down below, and I raced down to switch it off. A voice spoke behind me, making me jump high enough to bang my head on the deck above.

"Hello, David," said Dad, woozily. "What's all the noise?"

"Dad!" I shouted. "You're OK!" A fog-horn sounded nearby. "Just a minute – we're going to get rescued!" I ran back up the steps and blasted back with the last of the fog-horn gas. I looked out into the fog, and saw the glow from a search-light, sweeping from side to side and coming towards us.

Dad came up the steps and stood beside me. He seemed unsteady.

"Rescued?" he asked. "What do you mean, rescued?" He rubbed his head. "What's going on?"

"There was a fire. You were knocked out. I had to sail the boat on my own."

"Where are we?" he asked.

"On Jura. The far side of the island."

He looked amazed. "You sailed through the Corry? On your own? In this wind?"

I nodded. The search-light picked us out, and behind it I could see a bright orange hull. A voice came over the loud-speaker. "This is the Oban life-boat. Is the captain there?"

I looked at Dad. He looked back at me.

"You've just saved our lives and got us safely here, David. You're the captain of this boat now. You talk to them."

LIFEBOATS

Britain is a small island with a big coast-line, where the sea is often wild and rough. There are more than 200 life-boat stations scattered along our coast. Some have small rubber boats to rescue people close to land. Other stations have big, powerful boats for rescues far out at sea.

All of them are bright orange, to make them easy to see. The people who crew them are ordinary men and women who live by the sea, and are ready to be called away from work or home. They go out in the worst weather to save lives. They have rescued thousands and thousands of people over the years.

AUTHOR FACT FILE
STEPHEN POTTS

Are you a sea dog or a land lover?
A sea dog!

If you could sail anywhere in the world where would you go and why?
Venice. It's a city in Italy, built on the water along time ago. It's made for boats, buildings and people – no cars allowed!

Who would be your ideal cabin-mate and why?
Captain Cook, Britain's most famous sailor, from 250 years ago. He sailed all over the world, discovering lots of new places. With him on board I'd never have to worry about getting lost, or dealing with pirates.

Where would you least like to be shipwrecked?
Franz Josef Land – a group of islands near the North Pole. Most of the year they are cut off by ice. In winter it is dark for months at a time, and freezing cold. It's not surprising that no people live there – though hundreds of hungry polar bears do.

ILLUSTRATOR FACT FILE
NIGEL DOBBYN

Are you a sea dog or a land lover?
Definitely a land lover – I was once seasick for three days. Never again!

If you could sail anywhere in the world where would you go and why?
Antarctica. My wife has been there by boat and said the night skies were amazing.

Who would be your ideal cabin-mate and why?
My wife – because she's great company.

Who would you least like to be lost at sea with and why?
Hannibal Lecter – for obvious reasons.

What's your favourite marine animal?
The nautilus.

Where would you least like to be shipwrecked?
The island in *Lost*!

Barrington Stoke would like to thank all its readers for commenting on the manuscript before publication and in particular:

Rebecca Allan

Benjamin Barclay

Jade Bayne

George Antyny Chunilal

Margo Conway

Andrew McCaskie

Christopher Schweich

Robyn Shanks

Perran Thomas

J. Winter

Become a Consultant!

Would you like to give us feedback on our titles before they are published? Contact us at the email address below – we'd love to hear from you!

info@barringtonstoke.co.uk
www.barringtonstoke.co.uk